【Illustration】

THE MASTER

TELLS STORIES

《Contents》

Two-Headed Bird

When one truly wishes to engage in the practice of freeing himself
from the afflictions of greed, anger, delusion, suspicion and arrogance,
he will begin to transcend his worldly concerns.

This is a story of a two-headed bird by the Buddha.

There was a two-head bird. The heads took turns resting, so one head could always be on the lookout.

Actually, one of them had to be on guard most of the time because the other one was always asleep.

When they ate, the alert head would wake up the sleepy one to eat, who would fall right back to sleep afterward.

One day…

Hey! I'm so tired. Gonna need a rest. You go ahead be on guard.

As it fell asleep, a breeze blew down a fruit which was ripe and smelled good from a nearby tree.

This fruit landed right by the bird.

I guess I needn't wake him up for this. Since we are one, it wouldn't matter whether he or I eat it.

3

So the alert head ate the whole fruit by itself.

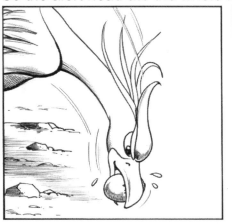 

What did you eat?
What is it that smells
so sweet?

It was a ripe fruit I
ate. I didn't want
to wake you,

so I ate it
myself.

Why didn't you wake me
up to enjoy it? All right,
one day I'll get even!

Sounds good !

Today, I'll be on
guard. Won't you
go rest up a bit!

Some time later...

4

There was another fruit blew down from the tree...

But this time, it was poisonous!

I'll eat this and we'll die together!

With a heart full of hatred, he ate it!

That sleepy head was Devadatta so many lives ago , and the alert head was I!

From this story, we know that the most difficult thing to control is the mind. Devadatta was the Buddha's cousin and disciple, but the Buddha still couldn't teach him the first thing about controlling the mind.

You cannot depend on anyone else for your own spiritual growth. When one truly wishes to engage in the practice of freeing himself from the afflictions of greed, anger, delusion, suspicion and arrogance, he will begin to transcend his worldly concerns. In the example of a two-headed bird, the head with hatred and vengeance ultimately caused its own demise as well as the other one. Good riddance!

A Shrewd Monkey

A truly successful person is loved
and respected by his peers.
Everyday, be careful what you think in your heart.

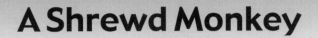

In the mountains, there was a family of monkeys who lived in harmony.

One of them was shrewd and wanted everything his way.

Others stayed away from him, but he wasn't bothered by it.

Why do you guys treat me like this? I'm the smartest! Fine!

One day, hunters came to the mountains...

The monkeys quickly ran for their life.

The shrewd one was unafraid, though. He made fun of them instead.

The hunters got so mad they were determined to kill him.

Let's get him!

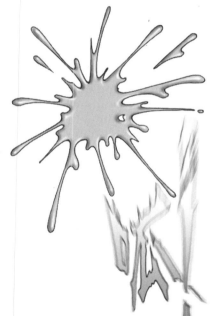

Serenity in life comes from harmonious relationship with people. Those few proud ones often find themselves alone.

The monkey's wits were no match for all the arrows that shot and killed him.

Had that monkey not been so proud, he would have lived. What a pity!

Be kind to people and never think you are above them in any way.

Otherwise, you stick out like a sore thumb and will be ostracized from the group.

Those people cannot have a happy life; they have only themselves to blame.

No man is an island. A truly successful person is loved and respected by his peers. Everyday, be careful of what you think in your heart.

Animals
Who Know Gratitude

If every person can give to others with gratitude,
our world will be a pure and peaceful place.

One day, a group of monks were discussing ways to carry out spiritual cultivation.

There is this Brahman who devotes his life serving the needs of his 500-member congregation so they can carry out their spiritual practice worry free.

The monks all had high regard for the Brahman.

After they had prostrated themselves before him, they told the Buddha about the Brahman.

What are you all talking about?

Your Holiness!

This Brahman has been serving others selflessly even in his previous life.

The Buddha recounted how this Brahman actively engaged in spiritual cultivation deep in the woods...

When one day a drought hit, and all the rivers and creeks ran dry.

Everyday he would travel far and with hollow bamboo stems fetch water for the animals.

Yet he spent very little time finding food for himself.

He grew weaker each day from over-exhaustion but was determined to carry on.

Worried about his health, the animals got together to discuss ways of repaying his kindness.

Get food and fruits anyway you can. Let's all do what we can to help him.

So the animals went off to search for food.

The Brahman was deeply touched by their acts of gratitude. He was convinced that every living being possesses Buddha nature.

Giving is not just about giving material goods. Acts of service with joy constitute giving as well.

This practitioner could serve so many people and animals because he had love and persistence.

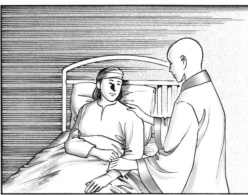

Tzu Chi is a world full of givings. One can give his money or labor. Those on the receiving end are also "giving" people an opportunity to help as well.

If every person can give to others with gratitude, our world will be a pure and peaceful place. If everyone can respect and care about one another, our society will be filled with brightness and warmth.

Japanese Kendo Master

There is no short cut to learning.
Develop your patience and confidence from it.

A Japanese father wished his son to become a great kendo master and asked his friend to teach.

The master knew he'd travelled far and was talented, but said...

Kendo is not easily mastered!

Will it take long to master it?

It will take your entire life.

Oh

My father will not want me to spend my entire life here.

Well, let's say 10 years.

The young man thought that was too long.

All right, 30 years then!

What! I'll do anything you want. Show me how to do it fast.

Impatience will not help you learn kendo. Why don't you plan to spend 70 years on it!

19

Sigh! I'm already here. Better do what he asks.

From that day on, he did nothing but menial labor such as cooking and cleaning the house.

Three years had gone by, and he felt he had learned nothing.

He missed his parents and was feeling sorry for himself.

Out of the blue...

The master struck him from behind, almost knocked him unconscious.

Everyday his master would repeat this stunt unexpectedly.

Soon he had developed a keen sense of awareness.

Finally...

Now you have what it takes to learn kendo. Follow my lead now.

The young man practices diligently with all his heart, and soon became a well-known kendo master himself.

There is no short cut to learning. Develop your patience and confidence from it.

22

The Farmer and the Hoe

Delusion and worries trap us
in the cycle of reincarnation.
It's like a rope that is all knotted up.
Only by giving up our attachments
can we ever hope to untangle it.

There was a farmer who tilled his field with his hoe day after day, year after year. He worked hard and his harvest was abundant.

Yet he wondered...

Tilling the field everyday is so boring. What does it all mean?

The monk looked happy and free, coming and going as he pleases. He was inspired to become one.

One day, a monk came to him and asked for food...

He picked up his hoe and stared at it. To him, letting go of it was like letting go of everything he ever owned. It wasn't easy.

Even though he made up his mind to become a monk, he somehow felt quite uneasy without his hoe.

OK, let's put it away!

He became a devout monk, but was still distracted with the thought of his hoe whenever he was near a field.

Often, he can't resist the temptation to run back home and look at the hoe again.

7 to 8 years later...

I seemed to have learned nothing after all these years. What's wrong?

Well, that must be it!

He decided to end the last remaining obstacle.

With that thought, he took his treasured hoe by a lake...

I've won!
I've done it!

Just at that moment, a king leading his victorious army happened to pass by.

What have you won? Why are you so excited?

I've won my own worst enemy. All my attachments are gone!

I should be happy with my victory, but I am not. What does the man have but I don't?

Conquering a land brings only a superficial victory, the king now realizes. Conquering one's own evils elevates one from an ordinary being to a saint!

"Forget about it, just let it go." is easier said than done. This is the reason it is called spiritual cultivation.

Delusion and worries trap us in the cycle of reincarnation. It's like a rope that is all knotted up. Only by giving up our attachments can we ever hope to untangle it. The farmer did not attain true liberation until he let go of his hoe-his last attachment.

A Life-saving Pocket

We were all born with a pure heart,
only to be clouded later by ignorance.
Work hard to return it to its pure state!

In a village, there was a family that had a boy who was a little slow but his mother loved him all the same.

When he started school, kids would make fun of him.

Here comes the fool!

But they cannot make him mad.

He was perfectly fine playing by himself.

For some odd reason, he liked to collect objects and carry them home in his pocket.

Everyday, his mother would wait and ask him to clear his pocket before letting him in.

When she forgot, he would bring them in and sometimes slept with them. This troubled her.

One day...

What's in your pocket today?

She was reaching for his pocket, but he wouldn't let her.

"What is it? Show me!"

The boy had no choice but to take "it" out carefully.

It was barely a nestling...

Honey, today is the Buddha's birthday, so take it to the field and let it go, OK?

As the boy complied...

Hold on, let me have your shirt so I can mend it.

The mother wanted to sew up the pockets so she wouldn't have to check them again.

When she was done, her son was no where to be found. Without his shirt, where could he be?

Soon, however, the grandma came home all mad...

How dare you let him run around the temple like that? I'm so ashamed!

She didn't know what to say. So she just stood there.

She couldn't understand why he'd gone to the temple and went looking for him.

She heard some noise from the storage room in the back...

Her son was holding a bottle of holy water he got from the temple.

Here. The Buddha will bless you. Open your eyes and go find your mama!

The boy gently fed the nestling with the holy water while talking to it.

The mother was deeply moved by her son's respect for life.

She decided to undo the pockets as they can also be used for saving lives!

The is a true story. Although this boy is considered stupid by other kids, he has a beautiful heart, and will not get angry when insulted. His grandmother, despite her constant visits to the temple, is still afflicted with a quick temper. The mother's unconditional love for her boy nurtures him well, and he will find good uses for his pocket.

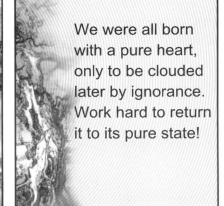

We were all born with a pure heart, only to be clouded later by ignorance. Work hard to return it to its pure state!

A Wise & Giving Old Man

Observe and think with an alert mind

so you can help yourself

and people see wisdom and overcome obstacles.

This story took place in a Japan seaside village that warmed people's heart.

The entire village went down the mountain one day to a Buddhist ceremony leaving an old man and his grandson.

Near sunset, the old man went out for a walk.

Suddenly, there was a tremor, but this earth movement was unusual, too.

He felt a certain wetness in the breeze, which seemed odd.

According to his grandpa, earthquake can be felt far away. He then looked out to the ocean...

My, the sea is turning black, and the tides seem unusual, too.

Usually tides rise and fall to a rhythm, but this time they fast approach like giant walls!

This must be the tsunami from aftershock!

Without hesitation, he quickly lit his own house and barn on fire.

The village people were still looking at the sea while someone noticed the fire.

咦?

"Hey, we gotta head back, the mountain is on fire!"

Everyone rushed back, but the old man didn't want the fire out yet.

It wasn't till everyone is back that the old man let them put out the fire.

Grandpa, how did the fire get started?

Grandpa's gone...mad! He lit up everything!

Look!

Everyone turned around and watched in horror.

The horrific tsunami uprooted houses and had them floating like matchboxes!

As the tides recede, the houses disappeared along with them.

The village people soon realized the fire was to save them!

Listen, observe and think with an alert mind so you can help yourself and people see wisdom and overcome obstacles.

The Karma of Monkeys

There is a false belief that gossipping
is nothing more than a harmless pastime.
It however often caused unwanted confusion
and misunderstanding.
Think twice before you open your mouth!

One time, one of the Buddha's disciples travelled a great distance to pay homage to him.

Having done the prostrations, he respectfully collected the Buddha's hair and nail clipping for people to worship.

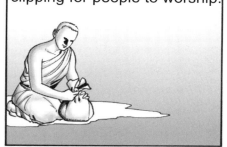

With the help of the hundreds of disciples, they built a shrine where the holy objects were displayed and worshipped.

The monkeys in the nearby trees saw this and decided to follow suit.

They piled up stones from a nearby creek as a shrine and paid their homage.

Suddenly the river overflooded one day...

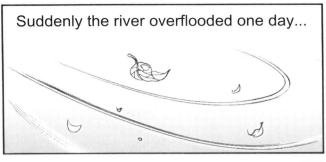

And all the monkeys were drowned.

Their spirits ascended to heaven.

They congratulated one another.

43

Then, they returned to the riverbank and paid homage to the dead monkeys.

Why aren't you in heaven but are instead prostrating to these dead monkeys?

They prostrated to the Buddha like the monks and we are now heavenly beings because of them.

There's someone like the Buddha? Beasts can be reborn in heaven?

To find more answers, they started on a long journey...

And arrived at last at the Buddha's abode.

44

The Buddha compassionately explained to them the imperfections of Brahmanism.

They all paid homage to the Buddha in great joy, but also wanted to know about the rebirth in heaven.

Many lives ago, a monk was building a shrine and had to take many trips up and down the mountain.

The Brahmans watching this made fun of the monk:

Look how he moves. Just like a monkey!

Even casual remarks like that can have dire consequences, let alone ones with hostile intent.

This slighting remark got them to be reborn as monkeys, but paying homage to the Buddha got them in heaven later.

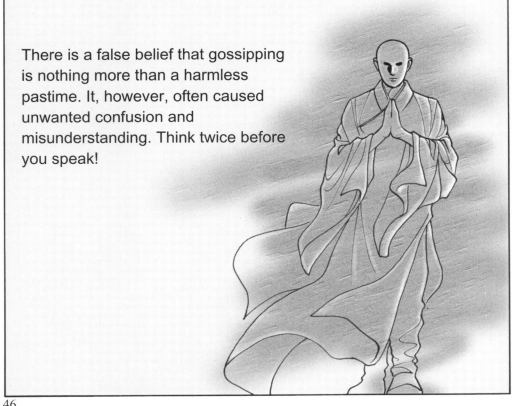

There is a false belief that gossiping is nothing more than a harmless pastime. It, however, often caused unwanted confusion and misunderstanding. Think twice before you speak!

The Monk and Viper

Thoroughly comprehend "kindness, compassion, joy, equanimity."
When hardship falls, we can still stay calm.

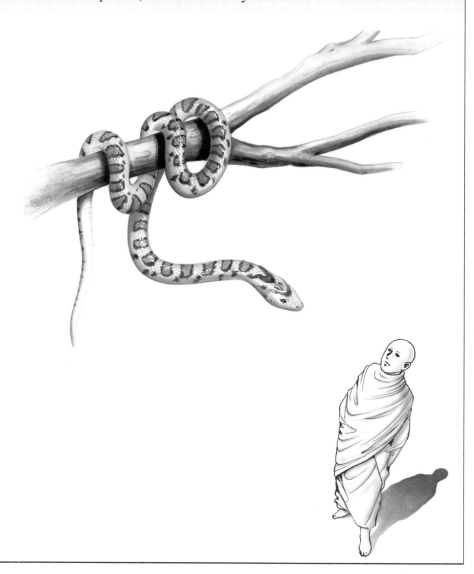

The Buddha used to take up residence for a period of time in the Abode of Bamboo Orchid Garden.

The monks would take up practice under the trees or in the caves.

One day, while a monk was meditating in a cave...

All of a sudden...

To his horror, there was a poisonous snake!

He swung his arm wildly but was bitten fatally in the wrist.

Shariputra!

What's wrong?

The snake got me. It looks really bad.

Shariputra got him out of the cave to rest.

Our body is only a temporary union of the four elements. Stay calm and know that life has no real substance.

Because he was a seasoned practitioner, the monk quickly regain his composure.

As the venom spread to the rest of his body, he died shortly.

Afterward Shariputra gave the Buddha an account of what had happened.

The Buddha was grief-stricken.

Snakes will not bite unless disturbed. Had he remained calm, he would not have moved his arm.

We shall all love and help one another, including all living beings.

Thoroughly comprehend "kindness, compassion, joy, equanimity." When hardship falls, we can still stay calm.

Travail of a Baby Leopard

Ordinary people are bound by the same attachments as this leopard.

Happiness is traded for misery.

Be careful where your heart wanders as

there can be disasterous consequences

A group of young men from the families of nobilities heard the Buddha's teachings and were inspired to join the family of monks.

But it was not long before they were disenchanted.

They were used to life's comforts and not ready to adhere to a monk's strict disciplines.

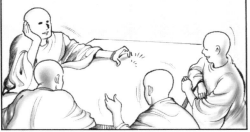

They often got together and talked about the old time and women they used to know.

All this did not go unnoticed by the Buddha.
One day...

Amanda, I'd like to have a few words with the new monks. Please get them here.

Yes, Your Holiness!

Their disorderly behaviors had an ill effect on other monks.

Ananda asked all the monks to come because he knew the Buddha wanted to address the issue to everyone.

Our new monks! Do you miss the good life you left behind?

They all bowed their heads down in shame.

The Buddha told them a story about the danger of having "attachment."

A baby leopard went out on his own to look for food...

But did not find any and was close to starvation.

When he suddenly found a dead elephant,

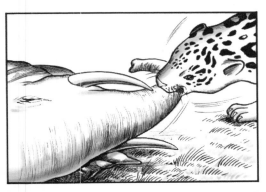

he was so excited he leapt for its nose but found it as hard as dead wood!

Other parts of the elephant were no better.

Even its tail was like a steel rope!

Running around it like mad, the starving leopard at last found the only place he could chew-its anus.

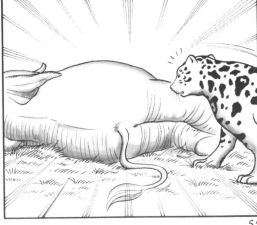

With excitement, he started gnawing at it, and quickly ended up in the abdomen.

What a feast! He gobbled up all the flesh and drank blood and slept with wild abandon.

In a few days, the elephant shrivelled up so much from the heat that anus was closed!

However, he was able to escape at last when the elephant started to decompose from rain.

Wow! I'm free. Look at all this space!

There was no way to get out no matter how hard the leopard tried.

But he found he had lost all his vitality and fur!

He looked like a monster because of soaking itself in the dirty blood and struggling to get out of it!

This came from having been bathed in blood for days and all that struggling to get out.

He gave up his free, spacious life for one that's inferior only to regret it later. But he longer was the same afterward!

Ordinary people are bound by the same attachments as this leopard. Happiness is traded for misery. Be careful where your heart wanders as there can be disasterous consequences

A Golden Arhat

Having a heart that is
"pure and serene"
is most precious!
Guard it well!

There was a farmer who used to enjoy his work and led a carefree life.

One day, when he was out in the field,

All of a sudden,

He dug out a pot!

He took it to the smith for inspection.

In the pot was a golden arhat!

Lucky you! This is all pure gold!

The arhats come in a set of 18. They are worth millions if you find the rest!

The farmer was beside himself with joy!

From that day on...

He labored day and night...

And tore up the field upside down!

The only thing he can think of now are the other 17 golden arhats.

Long forgotten are the days of leisure

and a carefree life...

The farmer gave up his leisurely life with his prized golden arhat.

If he could be satisfied, then his life would remain peaceful. However, greed fed on itself and soon engulfed his life and serenity.

Having a heart that is "pure and serene" is most precious! Guard it well!

Turtles and the Youth

It is truly beautiful
when people show love for all living beings.
Let us work together creating a luminous world
where the beauty of nature and all living beings
are appreciated and respected.

A youth and his father lived a simple life off a small farm.

Despite hardship, they lived a happy and content life.

As years went by, the father got older and weaker.

The youth had to work by himself but needed help.

One day...

The father wanted his son to go into town and buy a cow with his life savings.

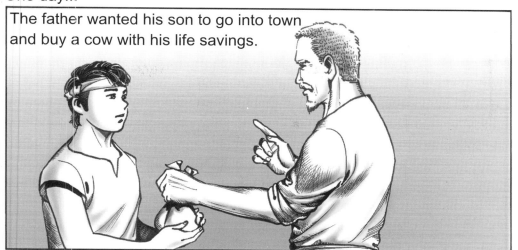

The youth walked and walked and found a rock to rest on by a creek.

There was a commotion and he went to check...

Kids were beating turtles that were turned upside down, and trying to get their heads come out.

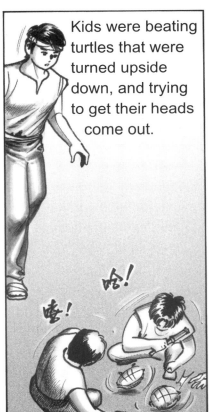

Of the five turtles, one seemed to be a parent and the others babies.

To him, it felt terribly wrong...

 Why are you doing this to them? They have feelings, too!

 We had to hunt for them! Mind your own business!

 Give them a break! They are a family and you're making them suffer!

 The kids just went on with their game.

But his pleadings fell on deaf ears.

The turtles were tied up and thrown about like a lasso.

The turtles were for sale, they said, but for a price.

He knew that'd cost most of the money he had for a cow,

but he went ahead anyway to save the turtles.

After they left...

He gently untied them and set the turtles free by the creek.

The turtles kept looking at him longingly.

Go! Get away before those kids come back! Don't let me worry about you!

The turtles seemed to understand and swam away, but kept looking back.

When he returned home, he explained the whole thing to his father.

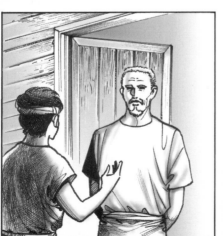

You did right, son! You saved five lives with the money. Don't worry about the cow.

Midnight...

There were knocks on the door...

Standing before him was a cow!

On its neck was a note that said,

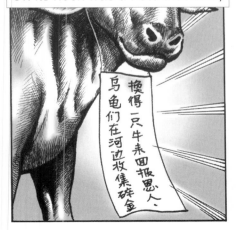

This allegory illustrates two views on life: one with compassion and respect for all living beings, and the other with total disregard for either.

It is truly beautiful when people show love for all living beings. Let us work together creating a luminous world where the beauty of nature and all living beings are appreciated and respected.

Fisherman and Eagles

It is dangerous for one to engage
in activities beyond his means.
Similarly, dharma practitioners
may run into obstacles
if he becomes too ambitious
and gets sidetracked!

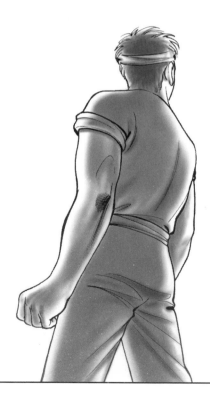

Out of the blue, an eagle started charging in.

A fisherman was selling his catch in the market, howling and hoping to attract customers.

It swooped down and took off with a fish as the fisherman yelled at it furiously.

It swooped down and took off with a fish as the fisherman yelled at it furiously.

Too bad I can't fly, or I'll let you have it!

On his way home, he saw a Ksitigarbha temple.

His wish was to become an eagle so he could fly.

Many onlookers grew curious of his newfound devotion

He wants to be like an eagle so he can fly.

Let's play a trick on him!

Right on!

The next day, one of them hid behind the statue.

Here's the fisherman!

There was a voice coming from behind the Buddha statue.

He again prayed to the deity.

You may try to fly from the tallest tree in the village.

Overjoyed, the fisherman ran into town.

He quickly found one and started climbing.

He grew concerned as he climbed higher.

Wow! Am I able to fly from here?

Look! Is that an eagle up there?

Surely an eagle knows how to fly!

I've turned into an eagle!

嘿！

He spread his arms and leapt up from the top of the tree.

啊！

Strangely he went straight down instead?

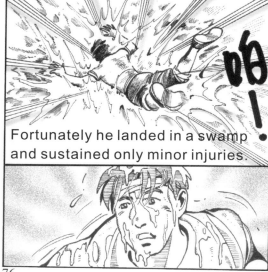

吧！

Fortunately he landed in a swamp and sustained only minor injuries.

It's my wings. I can still fly!

It is dangerous for one to engage in activities beyond his means. Similarly, dharma practitioners may run into obstacles if he becomes too ambitious and gets sidetracked!

Old Man and Burglars

This wisdom is called calm-abiding,
and comes from years of self-introspection that enables
one to face adversity and rise above it.

Subrub of Nara, Japan...

An old man and his daughter lived alone in an old house out of middle of nowhere.

One frigid winter, a snow storm hit unleasing freezing wind through cracks of the house.

They stayed sound asleep, however

Suddenly, the door swung wide open.

There were two burglars!

When they heard the snoring, they started snooping around.

But all they could find were two sacks of rice.

I feel so bad having you here when it's so cold.

Do you have any idea why we're here?

Oh sure, but I must apologize. I had a bad harvest and ended up with only two sacks of rice.

This much I owe you, but having you come all the way for it...

Here, please have some tea!

When did this happen?

It must've been karma in our past lives. Otherwise, you'd not have come to our house in the middle of nowhere at this hour of the night!

The other one suddenly got down on his knees.

I'm so ashamed of myself! Everyone says you're a good man, but we took you for a fool instead.

I wanted to be a good man, too, but life's hard. How can I ever be one?

My life is not any easier-but I'm still making good.

A life without material wants is truly worry-free.

You're a man of high characters.

Please take me as your disciple!

Far from it, let's both learn from each other!

The old man had been a diligent Buddhist practitioner, and was able to apply compassion and wisdom neutralizing an otherwise dreadful situation.

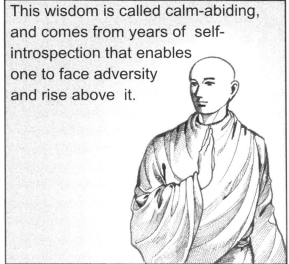

This wisdom is called calm-abiding, and comes from years of self-introspection that enables one to face adversity and rise above it.

The Exceptional Dharma Master Ming-Hui

Courage and perseverance come from actively cultivating your body, speech and mind.

Only then can one tap into his full potential for the benefit of all beings.

Long time ago, a Buddhist monk named Ming Hui had took up sanctuary in the mountains and was well-known all around.

When he was born, his father died shortly.

His mother soon died when he was three or four, and he lived with his uncle.

When he turned eight or nine, his uncle, wanting him to be a monk, sent him to a mountain temple with a servant.

The horse he rode was able to go on days without rest.

It just drank from the lake when it was thirsty.

How is he able to do that?

Perhaps it also wanted to get there soon.

He saw that persistence is the key to achieving one's goals.

After a lengthy journey in the mountains, they finally arrived.

83

An old monk would read stories to the child.

He was inspired by the Buddha's life stories, especially one where he gave up his life to feed the tigers.

The Buddha was at one life a kind-hearted prince. When he was in the forest one day, he saw seven starving baby tigers and their desperate mother.

Out of immense compassion, he offered himself to feed the tigers.

This story had a deep effect on the young monk. He vowed to have the same compassion and courage.

He often practiced meditating out in the wilderness all by himself.

It's getting dark. Where are you going?

After he turned 16, he set out for the woods one afternoon.

I want to challenge myself.

I read about the Buddha's courage and resolve, but now want to experience them myself.

Only a true practitioner can attain courage.

The old monk had no choice but to let him go.

In the forest there were man-eating beasts, but he was holding his own.

Serenity. Courage. Life is an illusion.

It was completely dark now and he kept reciting the Buddha's names. His mind was one with nature and he could hear everything ever so clearly. This was the Buddha's "No Fear" practice.

He finally found a rock somewhere deep in the woods.

Suddenly he saw two reflections in the middle of the darkness.

It dawned on him that he was looking at a black bear, but he stayed calm.

The bear quietly walked past him. He continued to remain calm.

Soon, the dawn broke.

Has your wish been fulfilled?

Master!

He realized his teacher must have been following him all night. Out of gratitude, he vowed to practice even more diligently.

The moral of the story was not to intentionally put yourselves in harm's way. Courage and perseverance come from actively cultivating your body, speech and mind. Only then can one tap into his full potential for the benefit of all beings.

A Treasure Watching Dog

An undisciplined mind is afflicted with greed in endless lifetimes
as it ties you down like a rope.
A true practitioner works diligently to free himself from it.

The Buddha passed by Elder Duti's house one day.

The elder was out, and a dog lying on a fancy sofa chair eating from an ornate bowl seemed to have all luxuries in life bestowed on it.

As it happened, it was its meal time.

When it saw him, it jumped out the sofa.

and barked fiercely at the Buddha.

You are still set in your ways! You've still got greed, anger and delusion even in this life!

Upon hearing this, the dog became sullen and quiet.

Soon, the elder returned.

He found the dog different as it just sat, not wanting to answer to him.

The servant told him what happened with the Buddha. The dog wouldn't even eat.

Anxiously the elder went and found the Buddha.

You are known for your compassion. What have you done to my dog?

Your love for this dog comes from the lifetime when he was your father.

The elder could not believe what he had heard.

How can you prove it?

He was a stingy man, and had hidden tons of treasures. He is back as a dog so he can keep an eye on them.

If you don't believe me, go back and ask him about them.

The elder went home after this.

If you are really my dad, show me the treasures.

When he was home, he patted the dog and asked,

The dog started scratching and sniffing under the sofa chair.

The elder was shocked by the dog's behavior.

He had men start digging. Lots of urns and treasures were found about a foot under the chair.

The elder started crying uncontrollably.

My dad can't let go of his greed and came back as a dog! How terrible!

An undisciplined mind is afflicted with greed in endless lifetimes as it ties you down like a rope. A true practitioner works diligently to free himself from it.

Buy Wisdom

One must always be mindful of his actions,
and make the best of his potentials.
This way,
he shall have forever serenity and joy as his reward.

Once upon a time, there was a country so wealthy it owned almost everything.

The king was unhappy, though. Nothing in life excited him anymore.

One day, he said to his minister.

Get thee to another land, and fetch me the fanciest thing you can find.

We have everything they have. What else can I get?

It's the king, however. So he got an importer to do the job.

What a drag! What can I buy?

He visited everywhere, but to no avail.

One day he saw an elephant.

Sitting on top was an elderly.

Wisdom for sale! Wisdom for sale!

That's odd. Can wisdom be bought?

What is this wisdom you're talking about?

Things you can see and measure all have a price tag, but wisdom cannot be seen or measured and is priceless.

Good. Let me buy it. What is it?

Here they are, "Think twice before you act. There'll be time for this." Forget not the ultimte truth in life.

Control your emotions so you will not do things you will regret later.

There'll be time when this advice becomes useful.

The man thought it made a lot of sense, so bought it with 500 ounces of gold as a payment for the "wisdom" and went home.

It was the fifteenth of August and the bright moon lit as he gently went in his house.

He saw two pairs of shoes by the bed which had veils on it.

One pair belongs to his wife, but what about the other one?

Insanity overtook him as he got ready to strike them with a bat..

Just then, a hand pushed the veils aside and there was his mother...

Wait, think!
Don't be rash!

Oh, son. Back so soon?

Mom! What are you doing here?

Your wife has a cold. I'm here to take care of her.

Cheap, very cheap indeed!

Son, why do you keep saying cheap? What is cheap?

There was a wise man. I gave him 500 ounces of gold for something you can't see called wisdom. It saved me from doing something horrible tonight.

The ultimate truth does not have a price tag on it. One must always be mindful of his actions, and make the best of his potentials. This way, he shall have forever serenity and joy as his reward.

The True Meaning of Happiness

Stay away from greed and do what you are supposed to do.
This makes a peaceful and worry-free life!

True happiness comes from serenity in life, not possessions as they seldom last. A life free of attachments is truly a blessed one.

This is a story about the peaceful life of a widow and her son.

Time to get up for school!

Time to get up for work!

Even as an adult, she needed to wake him up.

Mom, I'm home!

One day, when he came home...

Mom! You've worked so hard, but I've done nothing.

That's a strange question, he thought.

Why, sure.

I'd try to call you from downstair and sometimes have to go up for you. You always have a hard time waking up.

I don't want to see you one day not being able to sleep because of things you souldn't have done.

He knew what she meant right away!

I see. You need not worry anymore. We may not have a lot of things, but we are still happy, right?

Right! This peace of mind is what you can do for me, and it's called happiness!

Profit rightfully. Otherwise, you will not sleep well and not be happy no matter how much money you make.

Stay away from greed and do what you are supposed to do. This makes a peaceful and worry-free life!

Queen Luminosity

Achieve "beyond worldly paramita"
by giving without thinking of the giver,
gift or receiver.
Don't let your ego defile your heart!

In Japan over 1,000 years ago...

There was a princess whose complexion was as fair as moonlight, and everyone adored her.

Those who saw her would forget their worries, and she came to be known as "Princess Luminosity."

When she was about 14 or 15...

I'd like your permission to go out and see how people live.

As she walked around town, she warmly greeted everyone.

Her father gave the consent, knowning that she'd benefit from it, and had two attendants go along with her.

She was always smiling.

She's everything people say she is!

Her elegance and refined manners dazzled the onlookers.

When she walked by a fabric shop, there was a commotion inside.

Two people were disputing a sale.

You're short-changing me!

This is the exact length that you paid for!

The bickering got very heated.

She gently approached them and said,

Maybe there's a way for both of you to see eye to eye.

She took out a ruler and started measuring.

Look! This ruler will give you the exact length every time. You need not fight about it anymore.

Everyone was impressed by her wit as well as her grace.

In three years, she turned 18, and was made queen to Emperor Seibu with the title, "Queen Luminosity."

大悲院

She was a devout Buddhist, loved her people like a mother, and helped establish a sanctuary called "Compassion Abode" for the homeless and the needy.

A "Medicine Abode" was founded the following year giving away medical care.

113

She had by now gained a reputation as a bodhisattva, but wanted to do more.

Bathing house was a luxury then in Japan. She again urged the emperor to build 1,000 bathing facilities for the needy and would serve 1,000 of the handicapped personally.

The emperor was deeply touched and readily agreed.

She'd scrub the tubs everyday and help bathe the young, the old and the sick.

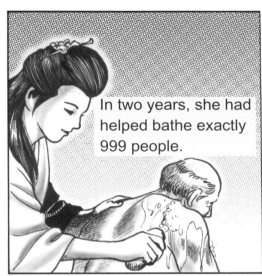

In two years, she had helped bathe exactly 999 people.

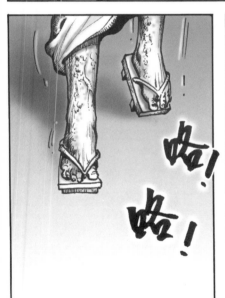

When the next patron showed up, everyone was shocked.

He had pus running all over his body and lost most hair due to it.

Everyone moved away quietly as the startled queen looked on.

She prayed to the Buddha for compassion and wisdom that she may help him without prejudice.

The prayer calmed her and she started scrubbing him.

I've had this skin disease for years. I was told it would take someone of noble birth to cure it, but he'd have to suck the pus from my skin.

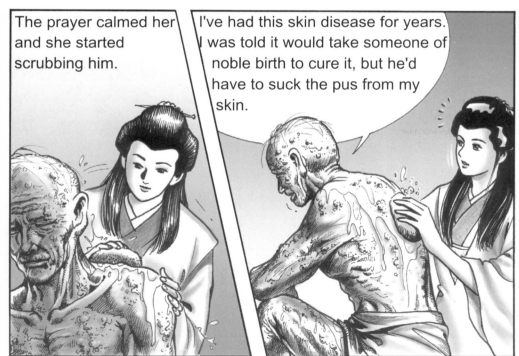

The old man seemed to be talking to himself.

Are you sure that will cure you?

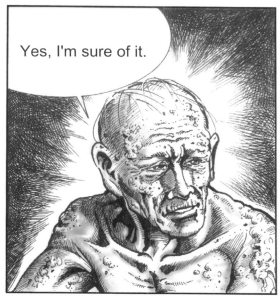

Yes, I'm sure of it.

If you are sure, then I will do it.

嗄？

Without a second thought, she bent down and started to work on the pus. Suddenly light and aroma shrouded him!

He transformed into Avalokiteshevara (Kuan Yin).

He then disappeared into thin air.

Elated, she felt that she'd done what others can't.

That night, a firm voice gently reminded her...

Watch out and don't be arrogant!

The queen felt ashamed, and realized she hadn't done anything special.

She was grateful of the timely warning and immediately repented before the bodhisattva.

She strived even harder to serve her people better.

She and the emperor were compassionate to their people, and Japan enjoyed peace and prosperity during their rule.

Achieve "beyond worldly paramita" by giving without thinking of the giver, gift or receiver. Don't let your ego defile your heart!

The Master Tells Stories · Illustration

Illustration : Lim Chor Yeow

Text Editor : Chew Ji Fan

English Translation : Richard K. Chang

CG : Chan Soon Beng

Cover : Ali Wang

Editor : Lo Yueh Mei

Published by the Tzu Chi Cultural Publishing Co.

Address : 19, Alley 7, Lane 217,Sec.3, Zhongxiao East Rd.,
          Taipei, Taiwan

Telephone : 886-2-2898-9000

Fax : 886-2-2898-9889

Postal Order : 14786031 Tzu Chi Cultural Publishing Co.

Fourth Printing May 2006

$ 150 NT©

ISBN : 986-7920-98-8   Printed in Taiwan